This book belongs to ...

Selena

Secrets of the Sands and Other Stories

How this collection works

This Read with Biff, Chip and Kipper collection is one of a series of three books at Level 6. It is divided into two distinct halves.

The first half focuses on phonics. It contains two stories: *Gran's New Blue Shoes and Ice City*. The second half contains two stories that use everyday language: *The Lost Voice* and *Secret of the Sands*. These stories help to broaden your child's wider reading experience. There are fun activities to enjoy throughout the book.

How to use this book

Find a time to read with your child when they are not too tired and are happy to concentrate for about fifteen minutes. Reading at this stage should be a shared and enjoyable experience. It is best to choose just one of the phonics stories or one of the stories using everyday language for each session.

There are tips for reading together for each part of the book. The first tips are on pages 6 and 36. They show you how to introduce your child to the phonics stories. Tips to tell you how you can best approach reading the stories with a wider vocabulary are given on pages 66 and 96.

Enjoy sharing the stories!

The **Helping Your Child to Read** handbook contains a wealth of practical information, tips and activities.

OXFORD
UNIVERSITY PRESS

Great Clarendon Street, Oxford, OX2 6DP,
United Kingdom

Oxford University Press is a department of the University of Oxford.
It furthers the University's objective of excellence in research, scholarship,
and education by publishing worldwide. Oxford is a registered trade mark of
Oxford University Press in the UK and in certain other countries

ISBN: 978-0-19-273438-9

1 3 5 7 9 10 8 6 4 2

Typeset in Edbaskerville

Paper used in the production of this book is a natural, recyclable product made
from wood grown in sustainable forests. The manufacturing process conforms
to the environmental regulations of the country of origin.

Acknowledgements;
Series Editors: Kate Ruttle, Annemarie Young

READ WITH
**Biff,
Chip &
Kipper**

Secret of the Sands

and Other Stories

Phonics

Stories for Wider Reading

OXFORD
UNIVERSITY PRESS

Tips for Reading *Gran's New Blue Shoes*

Children learn best when learning is fun.

- Talk about the title and the picture on page 7, and discuss what you think the story might be about.

- Identify the letter patterns *ew* and *ue* in the title and talk about the sound (phoneme) they make when you read them ('oo').

- Look at the *ew* and *ue* words on page 8. Say each word and then say the sounds in each word (e.g. *drew*, *d-r-ew*; *true*, *t-r-ue*).

- Read the story together, then find the words with the letter patterns *ew* and *ue*.

- Talk about the story and do the fun activity at the end of the story.

Children enjoy re-reading stories and this helps to build their confidence.

Have fun!

After you have read the story, find the eight pigeons in the pictures.

The main sound practised in this book is 'oo' as in *flew* and *glue*.

For more hints and tips on helping your child become a successful and enthusiastic reader look at our website www.oxfordowl.co.uk.

Gran's New Blue Shoes

Read these words

n**ew**	dr**ew**
ph**ew**	tr**ue**
kn**ew**	gl**ue**
fl**ew**	bl**ue**

Mum had some good news.
"Gran is going to meet the Queen,"
she said.

A car drew up. It was Gran.

"I am going to meet the Queen," she said.

"Good for you," said Mum.
"What great news."

"I will need to choose a new
dress ... and a hat ... and new shoes,"
said Gran.

Gran got a new dress. She had a
new hat and new blue shoes.

The time flew by. At last, Mum
took Gran to London. Biff, Chip and
Kipper went too.

"The Queen lives here," said Gran.

Oh no! The heel on Gran's new,
blue shoe came off.

Gran was upset.

"I can't meet the Queen with no heel on my shoe," she said.

"I can lend you some blue boots,"
said a lady.

"I can glue the heel on," said a
man. "I have a tube of glue in
my van."

A big car drew up. A flag flew
on the roof.

Chip ran up to the car.

"Stop that boy," called a man.

"Excuse me. Will you help us?"
called Chip.

The car stopped and a man
got out.

It was the Duke.

"The heel has come off Gran's new blue shoe," said Chip.

"I'll see what I can do," said the Duke.

"Wait by this gate."

Later, a man came to the gate. He had a box. It was full of blue shoes.

"You can choose from these shoes,"
he said.

Gran went to meet the Queen.

"I do like your shoes," said
the Queen.

"Gran's blue shoes will be big news," said Biff.

Talk about the story

What happened to Gran's new pair of blue shoes?

What was wrong with the blue boots?

How did the Duke help Gran?

What would you wear if you went to meet the Queen?

33

Rhyming words

Read each word on the blue shoe box.
Find a rhyming word on the red shoe box.

shoes   boot
blue   moon

flute   blew
prune   news

Children learn best when reading is fun.

- Talk about the title and the picture on page 37, and discuss what you think the story might be about.

- Identify the letter patterns *ce* and *c* in the title and *ss* and *se* in the story, and talk about the sound they make when you read them ('s').

- Look at the *c, ss, ce* and *se* words on page 38. Say the sounds in each word and then say each word (e.g. *c-i-t-y, city*; *g-l-a-ss, glass*; *i-ce, ice*; *g-ee-se, geese*).

- Read the story together, then find the words with the letter patterns *c, se, ss* and *ce*.

- Talk about the story and do the fun activity at the end of the story.

Children enjoy re-reading stories and this helps to build their confidence.

After you have read the story, see how many different ice animals you can find.

The main sound practised in this book is 's' as in *dress, city, nurse* and *palace*.

For more hints and tips on helping your child become a successful and enthusiastic reader look at our website www.oxfordowl.co.uk.

Ice City

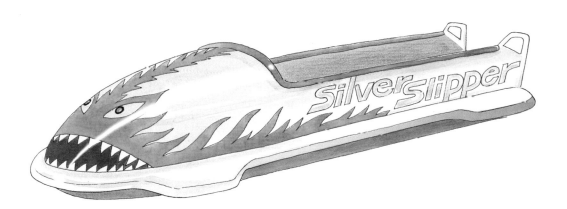

Read these words

city

ice

dress

prince

glass

palace

geese

nurse

Mum and Dad took the children to
Ice City.

"So this is Ice City," said Biff.

"What a place!"

"It's all made of ice," said Chip.

"This is so exciting."

They went to the Ice Palace. It had
scenes from fairy tales. They were
made out of ice.

"I can see Puss in Boots,"
said Kipper.

"And here is Mother Goose," said Mum.
"Look at all the geese."

"Guess who this is," said Biff.

"Look at her dress."

"See. It's Cinderella and the Ugly
Sisters," said Biff.

"The sisters were not nice to
Cinderella," said Kipper.

They went skating. Kipper did not
like skating.

Oh no! Biff hit Chip in the face.

It was an accident.

A nurse looked at Chip's face.

"It's fine," she said.

"We all need some dinner," said Dad.
"Let's go and eat."

They went to The Ice House.

It was made of ice.

They had a slice of pizza and
some juice.

"Even my glass is made of ice,"
said Kipper.

After dinner, Dad took the
children on the bobsleigh ride.

"The bobsleigh will bump,"
said Dad.

The ride began.

"It's like a real bobsleigh," said Kipper.

"It's exciting!" called Biff.

"It's like a real race," said Chip.

The sun began to go down.

"Look at Ice City in the sunset,"
said Mum.

"It's all lit up by the sun,"
said Chip.

The moon rose. Ice City went silver.

"It's all lit up by the moon," said
Biff. "It looks so peaceful."
"Time for bed," said Dad.

"What a super day," said Biff.

Talk about the story

How can you tell the family is on holiday?

Which fairy tale scenes did the children spot?

Why did Biff say sorry to Chip?

What would you like to do if you visited Ice City?

63

Missing letters

Find the missing letters by looking back in the story.

Pu__ in boots

Mother Goo__

_inderella   the prin__

Ugly _i_ter

Stories for Wider Reading

Children learn best when reading is fun.

- Talk about the title and the picture on page 67, and discuss what you think the story might be about.

- Read the story together, inviting your child to read as much of it as they can.

- Give lots of praise as your child reads, and help them when necessary.

- If they get stuck, try reading the first sound of the word, or break the word into chunks, or read the whole sentence again. Focus on the meaning.

- Talk about the story and do the fun activity at the end of the story.

- Re-read the story later, encouraging your child to read as much of it as they can.

Have fun!

After you have read the story, find all the clocks and watches in the pictures.

This book includes these useful common words:
thought   shouted   wasn't   could/couldn't

For more hints and tips on helping your child become a successful and enthusiastic reader look at our website www.oxfordowl.co.uk.

The
Lost Voice

Chip didn't feel very well. His throat was sore and he couldn't talk.

"Chip has lost his voice," said Dad.

"Oh no!" thought Floppy.

Mum took Chip to the doctor.

Dad took Biff and Kipper to school.

Floppy was all on his own.

"Chip has lost his voice," he
thought sadly. "I wish I could help
him."

"I know!" thought Floppy.
"I'll go and find Chip's
voice. I'm good at
finding things."

He wagged his tail
and ran upstairs.

Floppy ran into Chip's bedroom.
He looked under the bed. He found
a ball, a toy car, a sticky sweet and
a dusty sock . . .

. . . but he didn't find
Chip's lost voice.

Floppy looked in the toy box.
He found lots of toys and lots
of books . . .

. . . but he didn't find
Chip's lost voice.

Suddenly, the phone rang.
"There are voices in the phone,"
thought Floppy. "I bet Chip's voice
is in there."

Floppy hit the phone with his paw.
CRASH! It fell down. A voice said,
"Hello! Is anyone there?"

But it wasn't Chip's voice.

Floppy looked at the radio. "There
are voices in the radio," he thought.
"I bet Chip's voice is in there."

He hit the radio with his paw.

Nothing happened. He hit it harder

. . . and **harder!**

CRASH! The radio fell over
and someone started to sing.

"What a horrible noise," thought
Floppy. "That isn't Chip."

"I bet Chip's voice is in the television," thought Floppy. He ran to look. His paw hit the switch and the television came on.

Floppy saw a dog on the television.
It ran out of a shop with a big bone.

"Wow! That bone looks good,"
thought Floppy.

The dog ran faster and faster. A
voice shouted, "Stop! Stop that dog!"
"That isn't Chip," thought Floppy,
and he went back upstairs.

Floppy saw Teddy on Kipper's bed.
"Teddy!" he thought. "I bet Teddy
has got Chip's voice."

Floppy shook Teddy hard.

Grrrrrrrr! growled Teddy.

"Help!" barked Floppy. He dropped
Teddy and ran into Biff's bedroom.

WHOOSH! Floppy went skidding across the floor.

CRASH! Biff's clock fell over. "Wake up!" it shouted.

Floppy was scared. He hid under
Chip's bed and shut his eyes. Soon,
he was fast asleep.

Chip came home. He was feeling
a lot better now.

"Where are you, Floppy?" he called.

Floppy jumped up. "Chip has found his voice!" he thought.

He wagged his tail and ran downstairs.

Just then, Biff came in. Her throat
was sore and she couldn't talk.

"Biff has lost her voice," said Dad.

"Oh no!" thought Floppy.

Talk about the story

Why did Dad say that Chip had lost his voice?

Where did Floppy look for Chip's voice?

What do you think happened next?

What would Floppy find if he looked under your bed?

Hidden words

Help Floppy to get his bone by finding the words hidden within the words on the stairs, like this: h**is**

sticky

crash

Biff

growl

clock

shout

stop

has

his

Tips for Reading *Secret of the Sands*

Children learn best when reading is fun.

- Talk about the title and the picture on page 97, and discuss what you think the story might be about.

- Read the story together, inviting your child to read as much of it as they can.

- Give lots of praise as your child reads, and help them when necessary.

- If they get stuck, try reading the first sound of the word, or break the word into chunks, or read the whole sentence again. Focus on the meaning.

- Talk about the story and do the fun activity at the end of the story.

- Re-read the story later, encouraging your child to read as much of it as they can.

Have fun!

After you have read the story, find the letters and letter shapes hidden in the pictures that spell out the word TREASURE, and look for the desert rat.

This book includes these useful common words:
thought   suddenly   shouted

For more hints and tips on helping your child become a successful and enthusiastic reader look at our website www.oxfordowl.co.uk.

The Secret of the Sands

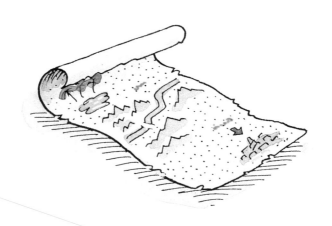

The children were playing on the
computer. They were playing Chip's
new game, Secret of the Sands.

Suddenly, the magic key began to
glow. "Look at the key!" cried Biff.
"It's time for an adventure."

Floppy growled. He didn't want an
adventure, but the magic was
starting to work.

The magic took the children into
a desert. They saw a boy riding a
camel across the hot sands.

The boy rode up to them.

"My name is Ali," he said. "You must come to my tent. You can't stay out in this hot sun."

Ali helped the children climb onto the camels. Floppy sat with Kipper.

"This camel is too bumpy for me," thought Floppy.

Ali took the children to his tent.

He gave them some cooler clothes.

Then he showed them a map.

"I'm going to the village on this map," said Ali. "Nobody lives there now, but long ago my father hid some treasure there. He called it the Secret of the Sands."

"Secret of the Sands! That's the
same name as my game," cried
Chip. "Can we help you to find the
treasure?"

"Oh yes! I'd like you to help," said
Ali. "Come on, let's go!"

They rode through deep, rocky
valleys and up steep, sandy hills.

109

At last, they came to the village.
There was sand everywhere. It had
blown into the empty rooms and
drifted over the walls.

"There must have been a
sandstorm," said Ali. "It all looks
different from the map. I don't know
where to look."

Wilf pointed to an old tower.

"That's the tower on the map,"
he said. "We must be very near the
treasure. Let's look here."

They looked into the shadowy
rooms and poked the sand with sticks.
"I'll help, too," thought Floppy,
and he dug some deep holes.

Suddenly, Floppy disappeared.

"Help!" shouted Biff. "Floppy has fallen down a hole. We must rescue him."

They climbed down into a hidden
room. Wilma shone her torch around
and something glittered in the light.
It was a treasure chest!

The chest was full of glittering
gold and sparkling jewels.

"The Secret of the Sands!" said Ali.

"How beautiful!"

The children put the chest onto
Ali's camel.

Suddenly, they heard a noise. It
grew louder and louder.

Two men on a motorbike came speeding towards them.

"They're desert robbers," cried Ali. "They're after the treasure!"

The children raced away but the
robbers came closer and closer.
  "They're going to catch us,"
cried Biff. "What can we do?"

Suddenly, there was a loud crash!
"Floppy has saved us!" shouted
Kipper. "The robbers have fallen
into one of his holes. They'll never
catch us now."

They got back safely, and Ali gave
Floppy a golden camel. "Thank you
for saving us," he said.

The magic key began to glow.

"It's time for us to go," said Biff.

The magic took the children home.

"What an adventure!" said Chip.

"What glittering gold!" said Wilma.

"What big bumpy camels!" thought Floppy.

Talk about the story

Why do you think the book is called The Secret of the Sands?

Why didn't Floppy like the adventure?

How did Floppy save the children?

What sort of treasure would you like to find?

A maze

Help Ali find the treasure.

Read with Biff, Chip & Kipper

The UK's best-selling home reading series

Phonics activities and stories help children practise their sounds and letters, as they learn to do in school.

Stories for wider reading have been specially written using everyday language to provide a broader reading experience for your child.

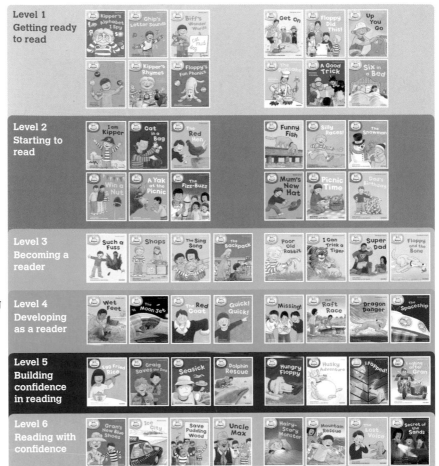

Level 1
Getting ready to read

Level 2
Starting to read

Level 3
Becoming a reader

Level 4
Developing as a reader

Level 5
Building confidence in reading

Level 6
Reading with confidence

Read with Biff, Chip and Kipper Collections:

Every collection includes phonics and stories using everyday language

Phonics support

Flashcards are a really fun way to practise phonics and build reading skills. Age 3+

My Phonics Kit is designed to support you and your child as you practise phonics together at home. It includes stickers, workbooks, interactive eBooks, support for parents and more! Age 5+

Read Write Inc. Phonics: A range of fun rhyming stories to support decoding skills. Age 4+

Songbirds Phonics: Lively and engaging phonics stories from former Children's Laureate, Julia Donaldson. Age 4+

Helping your child's learning with free eBooks, essential tips and fun activities
www.oxfordowl.co.uk